100 COUNTRY 'N' WESTERN GREATS

Wise Publications
London/New York/Sydney/Tokyo/Cologne

Exclusive distributors:
Music Sales Limited
78 Newman Street, London W1P 3LA, England
Music Sales GmbH
Kolner Strasse 199, 5000 Cologne 90, West Germany
Music Sales Pty. Limited
27 Clarendon Street, Artarmon, Sydney, NSW 2064, Australia

AM I THAT EASY TO FORGET

Words & Music: Carl Belew & W.S. Stevenson

THAT OLD TIME FEELIN'

Words & Music: Baker Knight

Don't let yes - ter-day's —— mis-takes keep us a - part —

'Cause that old time feel - in's

still in - side my heart

If that

(in - side my heart)

old time feel - in's still in - side my heart ——

WHEN MY BLUE MOON TURNS TO GOLD AGAIN

Words & Music: Wiley Walker & Gene Sullivan

VERSE

1 Mem-o-ries that lin-ger in my heart, _____ Mem-o-
2 (The) - lips that used to thrill me so, _____ Your ___
3 (The) - cas-tles we built of dreams to-geth-er _____ Were the

ries that make my heart grow cold; _____ But some
kiss-es were meant for on-ly me; _____ In my
sweet - est stor-ies ev-er told; _____ May-be

CHORUS

rain - bow turns the clouds a - way;_____ WHEN MY

BLUE MOON TURNS TO GOLD A - GAIN,_____ You'll be back in my

arms to stay._____ 2. The__ stay._____
3. The_____

D.S. al
Fine

11

I WON'T FORGET YOU

Words & Music: Harlan Howard

Till the breath in my bod-y is gone. _____ That's how it

C7

Ⓑ

is with me, _____ and you'll al-ways be _____ The on-ly love I ev-er

C7   F   G7

Ⓒ

knew _____ I'll for-get ma-ny things in my life-time _____ But my

C7   F   B♭   F

1

dar-ling I WON'T FOR-GET YOU. _____ That's how it

2

ritard.

YOU. _____

C7   F   F

ritard.

13

EARLY MORNIN' RAIN

Words & Music: Gordon Lightfoot

Guitar chords used in this composition

Bright

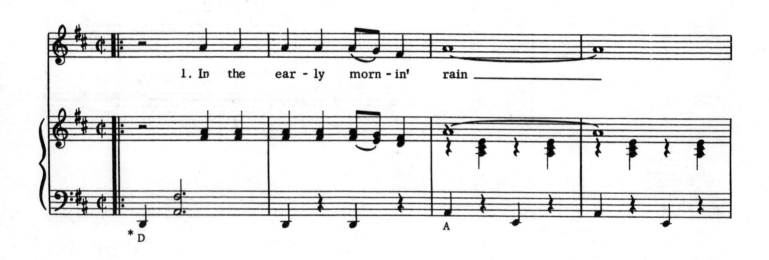

1. In the ear - ly morn - in' rain

*D   A

With a dol - lar in my hand,

A   G6   D   G6

* For Guitar: Tune low E down to D.

With an ach-in' in my heart

And my pock-ets full of sand,

I'm a long way from home, _____ And I

miss my loved ones so. _____ In the ear-ly morn-in'

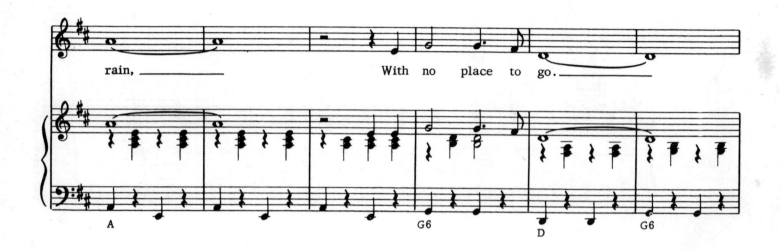

rain, _____ With no place to go. _____

A   G6   D   G6

Repeat 3 times.
Last time go back
to 𝄋 and use as Tag.

A   G6   D   G6   D

2. Out on runway number nine
   Big seven-o-seven set to go,
   But I'm stuck here in the grass
   Where the cold wind blows.
   Now the liquor tasted good,
   And the women all were fast,
   Well, there she goes, my friend,
   She's rollin' now at last.

3. Hear the mighty engines roar,
   See the silver bird on high,
   She's away and westward bound,
   Far above the clouds she'll fly,
   Where the mornin' rain don't fall,
   And the sun always shines,
   She'll be flyin' o'er my home
   In about three hours time.

4. This old airport's got me down,
   It's no earthly good to me,
   'Cause I'm stuck here on the ground
   As cold and drunk as I can be.
 * You can't jump a jet plane
   Like you can a freight train,
   So I'd best be on my way
   In the early mornin' rain.

 * *Repeat from here for Tag. (instrumental only)*

I'M GONNA BE A COUNTRY GIRL AGAIN

Words & Music: Buffy Sainte Marie

1. The rain is fall-in' light-ly on the build-ings and the cars, I've
2. (I've) spent some time in stud-y, oh, I've tak-en my de-grees, and
3. (I've) wan-dered in the hearts of men, look-ing for the sign, that

said good-bye to cit-y friends, de-part-ment stores and bars; The
mem-o-rized my for-mu-li, my A's 'n' B's 'n' C's; But
here I might learn hap-pi-ness, I might learn peace of mind; The

lights of town are at my back, my heart is full of stars,
what I know came long a-go and not from such as these,
one who taught my les-son was the south wind through the pines,
and I'm

Gon-na Be A Coun-try Girl A-gain. Oh, yes, I'm

Chorus

Gon-na Be A Coun-try Girl A-gain,_____ with an

old brown dog and a big front porch and rab-bits in the pen; I tell you

18

all the lights on Broad-way don't a-mount to an a-cre of

green, and I'm Gon-na Be A Coun-try Girl A-

To Coda ⊕

1. 2.

gain. _____

2. I've
3. I've

3.

D.S. al Coda 𝄋

Oh, yes, I'm

Coda ⊕

gain. _____

19

THERE GOES MY EVERYTHING

Words & Music: Dallas Frazier

Verse

1. I hear foot-steps slow - ly walk-ing, As they gent - ly walk a-
2. (As my) mem-'ry turns back the pag-es, I can see the hap-py

cross a lone-ly floor. And a voice is soft - ly
years we had be - fore. Now the love that kept this old heart

say - ing: "Dar-ling, this will be good-bye for-ev-er-more."
beat-ing Has been shat-tered by the clos-ing of the door.

Chorus

There goes my rea - son for liv - ing,

There goes the one of my dreams,_____ There goes my

on - ly pos - ses - sion, There Goes My Ev - 'ry -

1. thing.   2. As my thing._____

21

COTTON JENNY

Words & Music: Gordon Lightfoot

name. She wakes me up when the sun goes down,
sore", She rubs my feet while the sun goes down, and the wheels of love_ go
name. She wakes me up when the sun goes down,

round, wheels of love go round,_____ love go round,_____ love go

round,_____ a joy-ful sound_____ I ain't got a pen-ny for

To Coda ⊕

Cot-ton Jen-ny to spend_____ but_ then the wheels.go round._____

D.S. al Coda

2. When the
3. In the

⊕ CODA

Repeat and fade

round.

WHEN TWO WORLDS COLLIDE

Words & Music: Roger Miller & Bill Anderson

LEAVING ON A JET PLANE

Words & Music: John Denver

early morn, The taxi's waitin', he's blowin' his horn. Al-
think of you, Ev-'ry song I sing I'll sing for you. When
days to come, When I won't have to leave a - lone, A-

ready I'm so lone-some I could die.
I come back I'll {bring wear} your wed-ding ring.
bout the times I won't have to say.

Chorus

So kiss me and smile for me, Tell me that you'll

wait for me, Hold me like you'll nev-er let me go.

27

'Cause I'm Leav - in' On A Jet __ Plane, Don't know when

I'll be back __ a - gain. Oh babe, I hate __ to __

go. _____ 2. There's so go. _____ 'Cause I'm
3. ———

Repeat and fade

Leav - in' On A Jet __ Plane, Don't know when I'll be back __ a - gain.

UNTIL IT'S TIME FOR YOU TO GO

Words & Music: Buffy Sainte Marie

space   in the   lives   that we   planned, _____

stayed   out-side my   heart   but in you   came, _____

G   G/F#   G/F♮

To Coda ⊕

_____ and here we'll   stay   un-til it's   time   for you to

_____ and here you'll   stay   un-til it's   time   for you to

E7   Am7   D7

1

go. _____ Yes we're

2

go. _____

G   G

Don't ask _____ why, _____

Ab   F7   G

Don't ask ____ how, ____

Ab   F7   G

Don't ask ____ for - ev - er. ____

B   B7   Em

Love me ____ now. ____ This love of

Em   A7   D7

mine had no be - gin - ning it has no end. ____ I was an

G   G/F#   G/F♮   E7

oak, now I'm a wil-low, now I can bend, _____ and tho' I'll

Am   D7/F#

nev-er in my life see you a-gain, _____ still I'll

G   G/F#   G/F♮   E7

stay un-til it's time for you to go. _____

Am7   D7   G

Don't ask _____ why of me,

A♭   F7   G

Don't ask ⸺ how of me,

Ab   F7   G

Don't ask ⸺ for - ev - er ⸺ of me,

B7   Em

D. S. al Coda

Love me, ⸺ love me ⸺ now. ⸺ You're not a

A7   D7 sus4   D7

𝄌 *CODA*

stay un - til it's time for you to go. ⸺

Am7   D7   G

WICHITA LINEMAN

Words & Music: Jim Webb

I am a line-man for the coun-ty, ___ And I drive the main road

Search-in' in the sun for an - oth-er ___ o - ver load. ___
nev - er ___ stand ___ the strain. ___

I hear you sing-in' in the wi-res I can hear you thru the whine, ___
And I need you more than want you, And I want you for all time, ___

And the Wi - chi - ta Line - man   is still on the line. _____
And the Wi - chi - ta Line - man   is still on the line. _____

To Coda

I know I need a small va - ca - tion,

But it don't look like rain,   And if it snows, that stretch down south will

D.S. al ⊕ Coda

⊕ *Coda*

I LOVE YOU BECAUSE

Words & Music: Leon Payne

ST 064
032
T 105 TRO
n/cv 80

CHORUS

1. I LOVE YOU BE-CAUSE you un-der-stand, dear, ev-'ry sin-gle thing I try to do. You're al-ways there to lend a help-ing hand, dear, I love you most of all be-cause you're

2. (I) LOVE YOU BE-CAUSE my heart is light-er ev-'ry time I'm walk-ing by your side. I LOVE YOU BE--CAUSE the fu-ture's bright-er. The door to hap-pi-ness you o-pen

C C7 F C G7 C C7 F C G7

you._____ No mat-ter what the world may say a-bout me._____
wide._____ No mat-ter what may be the style or sea - son._____

I know your love will al-ways see me through._____ I
I know your heart will al - ways be true._____ I

love you for the way you nev-er doubt me_____ But most of all I
love you for a hun-dred thous-and reas - ons_____ But most of all I

love you 'cause you're you._____ 2. I
love you 'cause you're you._____

BLUE MOON OF KENTUCKY

Words & Music: Bill Monroe

40

SNOWFLAKE

Words & Music: Ned Miller

(Snow flake Snow flake Snow flake)

Snow was fall—ing when love came call—ing on this lone-ly heart of mine
Ice was break—ing and love was wak—ing in a win-ter won-der-land—

You were stand—ing there with snow flaked in your hair.
When I felt you slip your fin——gers in my hand.

Now snow is gleam——ing and I'm

thoughts were call ——— ing on ev ——'ry way I knew for
not dream ——— ing I know this is for real the

one ex — cuse to get ac — quan — ted with you.
love I have is too much to con — ceal.

B♭   C   F

C   G7   C

Chorus

then I said Snow flake my pret-ty lit —tle
Hey — ey — ey

Tacet ——————— *   F

snow flake ——————— ooh ooh the change in the weath-er has

C   G7

A BOY NAMED SUE

Words & Music: Shel Silverstein

ever did was be - fore he left, he went and named me Sue.____

Edim   F7   B♭

Verse II

Well, he must have thought it was quite a joke, And it

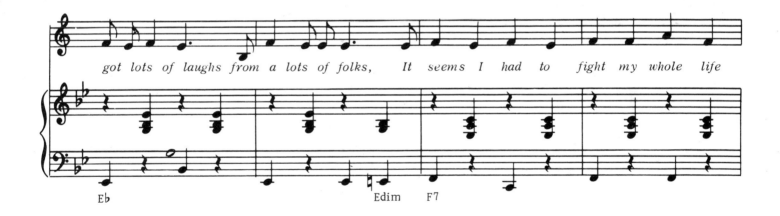

got lots of laughs from a lots of folks, It seems I had to fight my whole life

E♭   Edim   F7

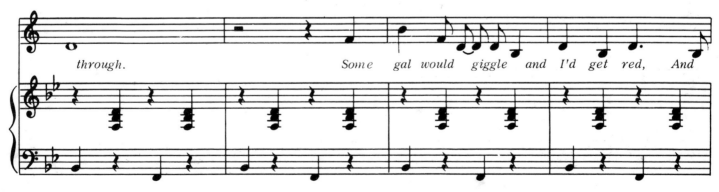

through.   Some gal would giggle and I'd get red,   And

B♭

some guy would laugh and I'd bust his head, I tell you, life ain't easy for a boy named

Eb   Edim   F7

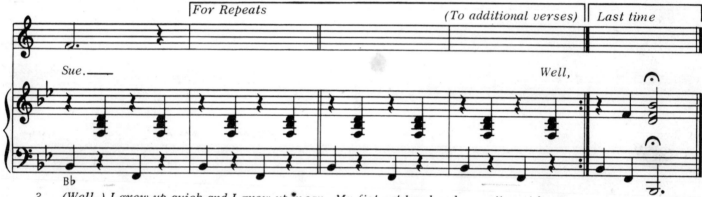

For Repeats   (To additional verses)   Last time

Sue.____   Well,

Bb

3. (Well,) I grew up quick and I grew up mean, My fist got hard and my wits got keen.
   Roamed from town to town to hide my shame, but I made me a vow to the moon and stars,
   I'd search the honky tonks and bars and kill that man that give me that awful name.

4. But it was Gatlinburg in mid July and I had just hit town and my throat was dry.
   I'd thought I'd stop and have myself a brew. At an old saloon on a street of mud
   And at a table dealing stud sat the dirty, mangy dog that named me Sue.

5. Well I knew that snake was my own sweet dad from a worn-out picture that my mother had.
   And I know that scar on his cheek and his evil eye. He was big and bent and gray and old
   And I looked at him and my blood ran cold, and I said "My name is Sue. How do you do.

   Now you're gonna die." Yeah, that's what I told him.

6. Well I hit him right between the eyes and he went down, but to my surprise he come up with a knife
   And cut off a piece of my ear. But I busted a chair right across his teeth. And we crashed through
   The wall and into the street kicking and a-gouging in the mud and the blood and the beer.

7. I tell you I've fought tougher men but I really can't remember when.
   He kicked like a mule and he bit like a crocodile. I heard him laughin' and then I heard him cussin',
   He went for his gun and I pulled mine first. He stood there looking at me and I saw him smile,

8. And he said, "Son, this world is rough and if a man's gonna make it, he's gotta be tough
   And I know I wouldn't be there to help you along. So I give you that name and I said 'Goodbye,'
   I knew you'd have to get tough or die. And it's that name that helped to make you strong.

9. Yeah, he said now you have just fought one helluva fight, and I know you hate me and you've
   Got the right to kill me now and I wouldn't blame you if you do. But you ought to thank me
   Before I die for the gravel in your guts and the spit in your eye because I'm the _ _ _ _
   That named you Sue."

   Yeah, what could I do? What could I do?

10. I got all choked up and I threw down my gun. Called him a pa and he called me a son,
    And I come away with a different point of view. And I think about him now and then.
    Every time I tried, every time I win and if I ever have a son I think I am gonna name him
    Bill or George - - anything but Sue.

FORTY SHADES OF GREEN

Words & Music: Johnny Cash

Moderately, with expression

1. I close my eyes and pic - ture the em - 'rald of the sea. From the
wish that I could spend an hour at Dub - lin's churn - ing surf. I'd

fish - ing boats at Ding - gle, to the shores of Dun - a -dee. I
love to watch the farm - ers drain the bogs and spade the turf. To

miss her lips as soft as ei - der -down. A - gain I want to see and do__ the

things we've done and seen.__ Where the breeze is sweet as Shal - i - mar, and there's

1.
for - ty shades of green. 2. I

D.C.

2.
for - ty shades of green.

rall.

49

I WALK THE LINE

Words & Music: Johnny Cash

3 As sure as night is dark and day is light,
  I keep you on my mind both day and night.
  And happiness I've known proves that it's right.
  Because you're mine I walk the line.

4 You've got a way to keep me on your side.
  You give me cause for love that I can't hide.
  For you I know I'd even try to turn the tide.
  Because you're mine I walk the line.

5 I keep a close watch on this heart of mine,
  I keep my eyes wide open all the time.
  I keep the ends out for the tie that binds.
  Because you're mine I walk the line.

CHESTNUT MARE

Words & Music: Roger McGuinn & Jacques Levy

And____ when I do I'll give___ her my brand._____

Verses (Spoken)

1. When I was up on Stoney Ridge, after this chestnut mare,

been chasin' her for weeks now Oh, I'd catch a glimpse of her every

once in a while, takin' her meal, or bathing. Fine lady,

53

can. _____ And ___ when I

do I'll give ___ her my brand. _____

And we'll be friends ___ for life, _____ She'll be just like ___

___ a wife. _____ I'm go-ing to catch that horse ___ if I

Verse 2. Then we were falling, down this crevice, 'bout a mile down I'd say,
I looked down and I see this red thing below us, comin' up real fast,
And it's our reflections in a little pool of water about six feet wide and one foot deep,
And we're falling down, right through it.
We hit, splashed that pool dry.
That's when I lost my hold, and she got away.
But I'm gonna try to get her again some day. (To Chorus)

JOLENE

Words & Music: Dolly Parton

Fairly bright tempo

Jo - lene, Jo - lene, Jo - lene, Jo-

lene _____ I'm beg-ging of you, please don't take my man _____

Jo - lene, Jo - lene, Jo - lene, Jo-

-lene _____ please don't take him just be-cause you can _____

_____ Your beau-ty is be - yond com-pare, with

flam-ing locks of au-burn hair, with iv-'ry skin and eyes of em-'rald green _____

_____ Your smile is like a breath of spring, your

voice is soft like summer rain, and I can-not com-pete with you Jo-lene.

He talks a-bout __ you in his sleep and there's nothing I __ can

do to keep from cry-ing when he calls your name Jo - lene __

And I can eas-'ly un-der-stand how you could eas-'ly take my man, but you

don't know what he means to me, Jo - lene. _____ Jo-

- lene, Jo - lene, Jo - lene, Jo - lene _____ I'm

beg - ging of you, please don't take my man. _____

Jo - lene, Jo - lene, Jo - lene, Jo - lene _____

please don't take him just be-cause you can. ___
ev - en though you

can. _____ Jo - lene ___

Repeat & fade ad lib.

Jo - lene _____

3. You could have your choice of men, but I could never love again.
   He's the only one for me, Jolene.
   I had to have this talk with you,
   My happiness depends on you
   And whatever you decide to do, Jolene.
   (To Chorus)

BALLAD OF EASY RIDER

Words & Music: Roger McGuinn

Flow_____ riv-er___ flow.___ Let your wa-ter wash

down___ Take me from this road to

some_____ oth-er___ town._____

Go riv-er___ go___

64

past a shad-y___ tree_____ Flow riv - er___ flow___

Flow to the___ sea_____ Flow riv - er___ flow___

Flow_____

to the sea._____

FOR THE GOOD TIMES
Words & Music: Kris Kristofferson

A LOSER WITH NOTHING TO LOSE

Words & Music: Kris Kristofferson

cared for_____ is gone,   I won't care _____ from now
hurts _____ an - y more,   noth - ing's worth _____ cry - ing

on, }
for, }   I'm a los - er _____ with noth - ing _____ to

to Coda ⊕

lose. _____ Noth - ing _____ to

lose   but the time   on my hands,

wait - ing_____ for no one_____ at all._____

Sift - ing_____ my dreams_____ thru my fin - gers_____ like

sand,_____ watch - ing_____ them die_____ as they

fall._____ 2. No more

D.S. %% al Coda

Coda

lose._____

BY THE TIME I GET TO PHOENIX

Words & Music: Jim Webb

time ____ I make Ok-la - ho-ma ____ she'll be sleep-ing, ____ She'll

turn soft-ly ____ and call my name out low, ____ She'll cry ____ just to

think ____ I'd real - ly leave her. ____ Tho' time and time ____

____ I've tried to tell her so ____ She just ____ did-n't know ____

____ I would real-ly go. ____

SOUTHERN NIGHTS

Words & Music: Allen Toussaint

Moderately, with a beat

men - tion the trees,__ whis - tling tunes that you know__ and love so.__
just be - yond the eye. It goes run - ning through your soul like the sto -

ries told of old. South - ern__ nights,__
Old man,__

just as good e - ven when closed your__ eyes.__ I__ a -
he and his dog that walked the old land,__ ev - 'ry

pol - o - gize _____ to an - y -
flow - er__ touched _____ his cold hand.__ As he

IF YOU WANT ME

Words & Music: Ben Peters

3. And so my friend, we can just let it end,
   Or go back and start again.
   What's it gonna be; remember what I say.
   It's got to be all the way.
   There can't be no in between, if you want me.

80

ACT NATURALLY

Music: Johnny Russell, Words: Vonnie Morrison

Guitar chords used in this composition

They're____ gon - na put me in the mov - ies____
hope____ you come and see me in my mov - ie____

They're gon - na make a big star out of me.
then I know that you will plain - ly see.

We'll make a scene a - bout a man that's sad and
The big - gest fool that ev - er hit the

3. We'll make a scene about a man that's sad and lonely,
And beggin' down upon his bended knee;
I'll play the part, but I won't need rehearsin'
'Cause all I have to do is act naturally.

IT'S FOUR IN THE MORNING

Words & Music: Jerry Chesnut

long - er I hold on and the long - er this goes on, The hard - er_____ it's gon - na
I love her so much, I don't know why I can't do the right thing and just let her

be;_____ } But it's FOUR IN THE MORN-ING and once more the dawn - ing just
be;_____ }

woke up the want - ing in me._____ 2. I've me._____

3. Last night, I told her, this time it's all over,
   Making ten times I told her goodbye;
   Last night we broke up, this morning I woke up,
   And for the tenth time I'm changing my mind;
   I saw more love in her eyes when I left her
   Than most foolish men will ever see;
   And it's FOUR IN THE MORNING, and once more the dawning
   Just woke up the wanting in me.

BORN TO LOSE

Words & Music: Ted Daffan

Guitar chords used in this composition

F G7 C Am E C7 Gm7 Dm7 F#dim G7sus4 Ab7

Moderately

BORN TO LOSE, I've lived my life in vain; Ev-'ry
BORN TO LOSE, my ev-'ry hope is gone; It's so

dream has on-ly brought me pain; All my life I've
hard to face that emp-ty dawn; You were all the

al-ways been so blue; BORN TO LOSE and now I'm los-in'
hap-pi-ness I knew; BORN TO LOSE and now I'm los-in'

BUMMING AROUND

Words & Music: Peter Graves

CRYIN' TIME

Words & Music: Buck Owens

lived to be a hund-red years old. Oh, it's

Chorus

cry - in' time a - gain, you're gon - na leave me,_____ I can

see that far a — way look____ in your eyes; I can

tell____ by the way you____ hold me dar - lin' That it

ENGLAND SWINGS

Words & Music: Roger Miller

Guitar chords used in this composition

Moderato (Whistle)

VERSE

Now if you huff and puff and you fin-'lly save e-nough mo-ney up to take your fa-mi-ly

on a trip a-cross the sea Take a tip be-fore you take your trip, Let me tell you

where to go, go to En-ge-land. Oh En-ge-land swings like a

pen - du - lum do, Bob-bies on bi - cy-cles - two by two, -

Eb   Bb 7

West - min-ster Ab - bey, the tow'r of Big Ben, — the ro - sy red cheeks of the

Eb   Ab 7   Eb

to ⊕ coda

lit - tle child - ren

Bb 7   Eb   Eb   Db   Eb   Db

VERSE 2

Ma - ma's old pa - ja - mas and your Pa-pa's must - ache, Fall-ing out the win-dow sill -

Eb   Ab   Eb

94

fro-lic in the grass — Tryin' to mock the way they talk- fun, but all in vain_____

Bb7   Eb   Ab

(to Chorus)

Gap-ing at the dap-per men with Der - by hats and canes.

D.S. %

al coda

Eb   Bb7   Eb

(Whistle)_____

CODA

Eb

Bb7   Eb   Bb7   Eb

CUT ACROSS SHORTY

Words & Music: Marijohn Wilkin & Wayne P. Walker

looks,   But   Short-y   must-a had   some-thing, boys, That

face,   He   knew   that___ he was   gon- na   win 'Cause Miss

hare,   When   Dan___ crossed the   fin- ish line, Well, he

can't   be   found in ___ books.

Lu-cy had fixed the ___ race.   "CUT A-CROSS, SHORT-Y," ___

found lit-tle Short-y___ there.

Is   what Miss Lu- cy said,   "CUT A-CROSS, SHORT-Y, ___

It's   you I want to win.   2. Now   win.

3. Now

97

DETROIT CITY

Words & Music: Danny Dill & Mel Tillis

Guitar chords used in this composition

C   G7   F   C7   D7   Bb

INTRO.

(1.) Last night I went to sleep in De-troit Cit-y, and I
(2.) Home folks think I'm big in De-troit Cit-y, from the

dreamed a-bout the cot-ton fields and home; _____ I dreamed a-bout my
let-ters that I write they think I'm fine. _____ But by day I make the

moth-er, dear old pa-pa, sis-ter and broth-er and I dreamed a-bout the
cars, __ by __ night I make the bars; __ if __ on-ly they could

CHORUS

I wan-na go home,_____ I wan-na go home;_____

Oh, how I wan-na go home._____

Recitation

Cause you know I rode a freight train north to Detroit City.
And after all these years I find I've just been wasting my time,

So I just think I'll take my foolish pride and put it on the
    south-bound freight and ride
And go on back to the loved ones, the ones that I left waiting
    so far behind. CHORUS

FROM A JACK TO A KING

Words & Music: Ned Miller

Guitar chords used in this composition

©Copyright 1957 by Dandelion Music Co., USA.
All rights for the British Commonwealth of Nations, (exc. Canada & Australasia), the Republic of Eire,
South Africa, Italy, France, Germany, Austria, Switzerland and Japan controlled by Burlington Music Co. Ltd.
All Rights Reserved. International Copyright Secured.

heart. _____ For just a lit-tle while, I thought that I might

lose the game ___ Then just in time, I saw the twin-kle in your

eye. _____ FROM A JACK TO A KING ___ From lon-li-ness to a

wed-ding ring, I played an ace and I won a queen, You made me queen of your

heart. FROM A JACK TO A heart. _____

GREEN, GREEN GRASS OF HOME

Words & Music: Curly Putman

there runs Ma - ry hair of gold and lips like cher - ries, it's
my sweet Ma - ry hair of gold and lips like cher - ries, it's

Bb7   Eb   Ebdim   Eb   Dm7   Cm7

good to touch the green, green grass of home.
good to touch the green, green grass of home.

Bb   F7   Cm7   F7   Bb   Eb

CHORUS.

Yes, they'll all come to meet me arms—
Yes, they'll all come to see me in the

Cm7   F13   Bb   Bb7

1 - 2

reach - ing smil-ing sweet - ly it's good to touch the

Eb   Cm7   Bb

103

green, green grass of home.   (2) The

shade   of that old oak tree as they lay me   'neath the

green, green grass of home. ────────

VERSE 3. (spoken) Then I awake and look around me
at four grey walls that surround me,
And I realize that I was only dreaming,
For there's a guard and there's a sad old padre
-arm in arm we'll walk at daybreak
Again I'll touch the green, green grass of home.

(to Chorus)

TOBACCO ROAD

Words & Music: John D. Loudermilk

IT WASN'T GOD WHO MADE HONKY TONK ANGELS

Words & Music: J.D. Miller

CHORUS

KING OF THE ROAD

Words & Music: Roger Miller

last time to coda ⊕

four bit room, – I'm a   man   of means – by – no means –   King of the road. –
big a – round, – I'm a   man   of means – by – no means –   King of the road. –
four bit room, – I'm a   man   of means – by – no means –   King of the road. –

C   F   G7

I know ev – er – y en – gin – eer on ev – er – y train –

C   C   C   F

All of the chil – dren, and   all of their names – And ev – er – y hand – out in ev – er – y town – And

G7   C   F

⊕ CODA

ev – 'ry lock that ain't locked when no – one's a – round. I sing

D.S. 𝄋

al ⊕ coda

G7 tacet – – – – – – – – – – – – – – – G7

C

THE LONG BLACK VEIL

Words & Music: Marijohn Wilkin & Danny Dill

Guitar chords used in this composition

slay - er who ran looked a lot like me. _____

The judge said "Son, what is your al - i -
scaf - fold was high _____ and e - ter - ni - ty

bi? _____ If you were some - where else then you won't have to
near, _____ She stood in the crowd and shed not a

die." _____ I spoke not a word _____ though it meant my
tear. _____ But some - times at night _____ when the cold wind

D7   C   G

G   D7   G

D7   C

G   D7

life, for I had been in the arms of my best friend's
moans in a long black veil she cries o'er my

G   D7   C

Refrain

wife. _____ She walks these hills in a
bones. _____

G   C   G

long black veil, She vis - its my grave _____ when the

C   G   C   G

night winds wail. _____ No - bo - dy

C   G

114

RELEASE ME

Words & Music: Eddie Miller, Dub Williams, Robert Yount & Robert Harris

waste | our | lives would be | a | sin,
lips | are | warm while | yours | are | cold,
live | a | lie would | bring us | pain,

re—lease me | and | let me | love a—
re—lease me | my | dar—ling | let me
so re—lease me | and | let me | love a—

F   Fdim Bb   F   F7   Bb

F   C7

1. 2.   **3.**

—gain.
go.   — gain.

F   C7   F

Bb   F

117

RUBY DON'T TAKE YOUR LOVE TO TOWN

Words & Music: Mel Tillis

To Coda

Ru - - by, _____ don't take your love to town. _____ For it

C   F   G7   C

was-n't me that start-ed that old cra-zy As-ia war, _____ But I was proud to go and do my

Dm   F   C   Dm

pa-tri-ot-ic chores. _____ Oh, I know, Ru-by, that I'm not the man I used to be, _____

F   G7   F   G7

D.C. al ✛ *Coda*

____ But, Ru - - by, _____ I still need your com-pa-ny. _____

C   F   G7   C

✛ **CODA**

____ For God's sake turn a-round, don't take your love to town. _____

F   C   F   G7   C

119

WABASH CANNONBALL

Words & Music: A.P. Carter

reg - 'lar com - bi - na - tion   of the Wa - bash Can - non Ball.
chan - ges can be ta - ken   on the Wa - bash Can - non Ball.

D7   G

3 . She came down from Birmingham
One cold December day.
As she pulled into the station
You could hear all the people say,
There's the gal from Tennessee
She is long and she is tall.
She comes from Birmingham
on the Wabash Cannon Ball.

4. Just listen to the jingle
And the rumble and the roar,
As she glides along the woodland
To the hills and by the shore.
Hear the mighty rush of the engine
Hear the lonesome hoboes call,
While she's trav'ling thru the jungle
on the Wabash Cannon Ball.

5. Here's to old man daddy Claxton,
May his name forever stand;
May it always be remembered
Throughout the land.
His earthly race is over
And the curtains 'round him fall.
We'll carry him home to vict'ry
on the Wabash Cannon Ball.

WELCOME TO MY WORLD

Words & Music: Winkler & Hathcock

heart, _____ Leave your cares be - hind; _____ WEL-COME TO MY

WORLD _____ Built with you in mind. _____

Knock   and the door_ will o - pen; ___ Seek   and   you will

find.   Ask   and you'll   be giv-en_____ The

key to this world of mine. _____ I'll be wait-ing

here _____ With my arms un-furled, _____ Wait-ing just for

you; _____ WEL-COME TO MY WORLD, _____ WEL-COME TO MY

WEL-COME TO MY WORLD. _____

meno mosso　　　　　　　　　*rall.*

124

MY TENNESSEE MOUNTAIN HOME

Words & Music: Dolly Parton

1. Sit - ting on the front porch on a sum - mer af - ter - noon, in a straight - back chair on two legs leaned a - gainst the wall. Watch the kids ___ a - play - ing ___ with

June bugs on a string, And chase the glow - ing

fire - flies when eve - ning's shad - ows fall.

CHORUS

In my Ten - nes - see___ Moun - tain___

home, life is as peace - ful as a ba - by's___

2. Honeysuckle vines cling to the fence along the lane,
   And their fragrance makes the summer wind so sweet,
   And on a distant hilltop, an eagle spreads its wings,
   And a song bird on a fence post sings a melody.
   (Repeat Chorus)

3. Walking home from church on Sunday with the one you love,
   Just laughing, talking, making future plans,
   And when the folks ain't looking, you might steal a kiss or two,
   Sitting in the porch swing holding hands.
   (Repeat Chorus)

COAT OF MANY COLORS

Words & Music: Dolly Parton

wore it so proud - ly _____ Al - though we had no
if they choose to be _____ Now I know we had no

mon - ey I was rich as I could be in my coat of man - y
mon - ey but I was rich as I could be in my coat of man - y

To Coda ⊕   *D.S. al Coda* 𝄋

col - ors my ma - ma made for me. _____ So with
col - ors my

Coda ⊕

ma - ma made _ for me _____ she made for me. _____

131

FOLSOM PRISON BLUES

Words & Music: Johnny Cash

drag - gin' on. _____
watch him die. _____

But that train ___ keeps ___ roll - in' ___ on down to
When I hear that whis - tle blow - in' I hang my

San ___ An - tone. _____ 2. When
head ___ and ___ cry. _____

3. I bet there's rich folks eatin' in a fancy dining car.
   They're prob'ly drinkin' coffee and smokin' big cigars,
   But I know I had it comin', I know I can't be free,
   But those people keep a-movin', and that's what tortures me.

4. Well, if they freed me from this prison, if that railroad train was mine,
   I bet I'd move on over a little farther down the line,
   Far from Folsom Prison, that's where I want to stay,
   And I'd let that lonesome whistle blow my blues away.

DESPERADO

Words & Music: Don Henley & Glenn Frey

so long now.___ Oh, you're a hard one, I know that

you got your rea - sons, these things that are pleas - in' you___ can

hurt you some-how. Don't you draw the queen___ of dia - monds,_ boy,_ she'll

beat you if she's a - ble,___ you know the queen of hearts_ is al - ways your best bet.___

Now it seems to me_ some fine_ things_ have been laid up-on_ your ta - ble, but you on - ly want_ the ones_ that you can't_ get._ Des - per - a - do, oh, you ain't_ get-tin' no young - er,_ your pain and your hun - ger,_ they're

day. _____ You're los - in' all__ your highs__ and lows.__ Ain't it

fun-ny how__ the feel - in' goes__ a - way? _____

____ Des - per-a - do, why don't__ you

come to your sens - es? Come down from your fenc - es, _____

138

139

SOMEONE TO LAY DOWN BESIDE ME

Words & Music: Karla Bonhof

DELTA DAY (No Time To Cry)

Words & Music: Kris Kristofferson & Marijohn Wilkin

Dawn _____ breaks _____ and I feel trop-i-cal rain fall down on

Love _____ of life _____ and one sem-i-au-to-mat-ic ri-fle to a shoul-der

all here be-low _____ on the ground. _____

sure made a man _____ out of me. _____

cry. _____ Warm

whis - pers, soft _____ sum - mer laugh - ter "I

love you's" don't fade a - way old

feel - ings al - most for - got - ten wait for

me just one more Del - ta day.____

Night____ falls so soft____ on the dead and hard on the liv - ing,

si - lent and still____ where we lay.____ Oh,____

____ God, pro - tect us the chil - dren of a mis - un - der - stand - ing,

146

SHAKE HANDS WITH THE DEVIL

Words & Music: Kris Kristofferson

I don't like be - liev - ing that I'm e - vil in your
I can take you high - er than you've ev - er been be -

eyes, but I ain't make be - liev - ing I'm a
fore and show you things you nev - er dared to

saint, 'cause I'll do an - y -
see. And hand in hand to -

thing I can to win you from the world, it's
geth - er we can laugh the world a - way, I'll

I don't want your sil - ver or your gold.

I'm not af - ter an - y - thing that you don't want to give me, I just want your bod - y and your soul.

soul.

soul.

DAYTIME FRIENDS

Words & Music: Ben Peters

Chorus

154

o - ver there's no peace of

mind, Just a long-ing for___ the way___ things should have

been. And she won - ders

why some men nev - er find___ That a

156

wom-an needs_ a lov - er and a friend: Day-time friends_

and night-time lov - ers,_ Hop-in' no one else_ dis-

cov-ers where they go,_ what they do_ in their se-

- cret hide - a-way.___ Day-time friends_ and night-time lov-

ers,_____ they don't wan - na hurt_____ the oth-

er, So they love____ in the night - time and shake hands__

1.
____ in the light of day.

2.
D. S. and fade

Day-time friends_____ in the light of day.__ Day-time friends__

158

OLD SHEP

Words & Music: Clyde (Red) Foley

1. When I was a lad, and old Shep was a pup, O'er hills and
2. (So the) years rolled a long, and at last he grew old, His eye-sight was
3. (I) went to his side and sat on the ground, He laid his

mead-ows we'd roam,_____ Just a boy and his dog We were
fast grow-ing dim,_____ Then one day the doc - tor looked
head on my knee,_____ I stroked the best pal that a

both full of fun We grew up to geth-er that way. _____ I re-
at me and said I can't do no more for him, Jim. _____ With a
man ev er found I cried so I scarce-ly could see. _____ Old

F7   Bb Cdim Bb7   Eb   Eb7

-mem-ber the time at the old swim-ming hole, When I would have
hand that was tremb-ling I picked up my gun, I aimed it at
Shep-pie he knew he was go ing to go, For he reached out and

Ab   Eb7   Abm6   Eb

drowned be-yond doubt _____ Shep was right there to the res-cue he
Shep's faith-ful head _____ I just could-n't do it I want-ed to
licked at my hand_____ He looked up at me, just as much as to

Bbdim   Bb7   Eb   C7   F7

1.2.3

came   He   jumped in   and   helped pull me   out._____ 2. So the
run   And I wished that they'd shoot me in - stead._____ 3. I
say   We're part - ing, but you un - der - stand._____ Now

B♭7   Cdim   B♭7   E♭ Cdim B♭7

old Shep is   gone, where the   good dog - gies   go   And no   more with old

E♭   B7   B♭7   E♭   Cm

Shep   will I   roam _____   But if dogs   have a   heav - en, there's

F7   B♭7   E♭   C7

one thing I   know   Old Shep has   a   won - der - ful   home._____

Fine

F7   B♭   Cdim   B♭7 E♭ B♭7 E♭

161

SHE BELIEVES IN ME

Words & Music: Steve Gibb

try to get_ un - dressed_with-out the light.___ Then qui - et - ly_ she says, "How was your

night?" And I come to her_ and say_____ it was all right. And I

hold her tight.__ And she be - lieves in me.

I'll nev-er know just what she sees_____ in me.__ I told her some-day_ if she

163

WE DON'T MAKE LOVE ANYMORE

Words & Music: Kenny Rogers & Marianne Gordon

*Guitarists: Play finger style

SEND ME THE PILLOW YOU DREAM ON

Words & Music: Hank Locklin

Send me the pil-low_ that you dream on,_____

Don't you know that I still care for you?_____

Send me the pil-low_ that you dream on,_____ So,

HIGH NOON

Words : Ned Washington. Music: Dimitri Tiomkin

RING OF FIRE

Words & Music: Merle Kilgore & June Carter

Moderately Bright

Love _____ is a burn-ing thing _____
taste _____ of_ love is sweet _____

And it makes _____ a fi - ry
When_ hearts _____ like ours _

ring

beat

Bound _____ by wild de - sires _____

I fell for you like a child _____

I fell in - to a Ring Of Fire._____

Oh, but the fire went wild._____

I fell in - to a burn-ing Ring Of Fi - re I went

SHE THINKS I STILL CARE

Words & Music: Dicky Lee

JACKSON

Words & Music: Billy Edd Wheeler & Gaby Rogers

COUNTRY COMFORT

Words & Music: Elton John & Bernie Taupin

Count-ry   Com-fort's   an-y truck that's go - in'

Last time to Coda

home.

3. (Down at the)
4. (Now the)

D.S. for extra verses

3. Down at the well they've got a new machine,
   Foreman says it cuts manpower by fifteen,
   But that ain't natural, so old Clay would say,
   He's a horse-drawn man until his dying day.

   (Repeat Chorus)

4. Now the old fat goose is flying 'cross the sticks,
   The hedge-hog's done in clay between the bricks,
   And the rocking chair's a-creaking on the porch,
   Across the valley moves the herdsman with his torch.

   (Repeat Chorus)

Coda

home.—   Coun-try Com-fort's an-y truck that's go-ing back   home.—   Coun-try

Com-fort's   an-y truck that's go-ing back   home.—

IN THE MISTY MOONLIGHT

Words & Music: Cindy Walker

sea sand, ___ If your hand's in my hand, ___ I won't ___ be

blue. 'Way up on the moun-tain, ___ Or 'way down in the

val-ley, ___ I know I'll be hap-py, ___ An - y place, an - y -

where, I don't care. In The Mist-y Moon-light, ___ By the flick - 'ring

Repeat for fade

SEA OF HEARTBREAK

Words & Music: Hal David & Paul Hampton

a - way from the sea _____ This Sea Of Heart - break

And lost love_ lone - li - ness, Mem-'ries of your ca - ress, so di - vine

How I wish you were mine a - gain, my dear___ I'm on a sea of tears__

_ A Sea Of Heart - break _____

rit.

195

(THAT'S WHAT YOU GET) FOR LOVIN' ME

Words & Music: Gordon Lightfoot

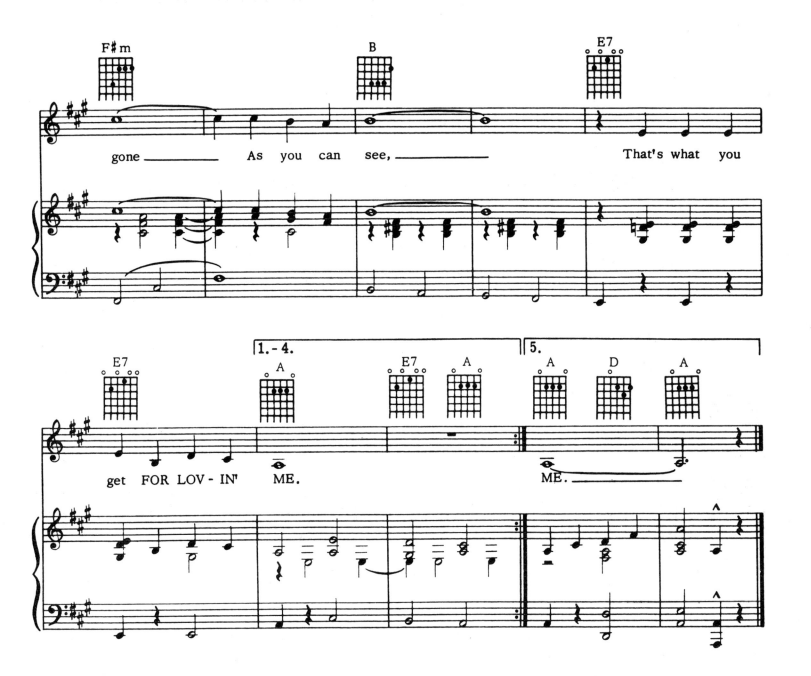

2. I ain't the kind to hang around
With any new love that I found
'Cause movin' is my stock in trade
I'm movin' on,
I won't think of you when I'm gone.

3. So don't you shed a tear for me,
I ain't the love you thought I'd be,
I got a hundred more like you,
So don't be blue,
I'll have a thousand 'fore I'm through.

4. Now, there you go you're cryin' again,
Now, there you go you're cryin' again,
But then, some day, when your poor heart
Is on the mend,
Well, I just might pass this way again.

5. That's what you get for lovin' me,
That's what you get for lovin' me,
Well, ev'rything you had is gone
As you can see,
That's what you get for lovin' me.

TUPELO HONEY

Words & Music: Van Morrison

1. You can take all the tea in Chi-na, put it in a big brown bag for me. Sail right round all the sev-en o-ceans, drop it straight in-to the deep-blue sea.

©Copyright 1971 WB Music Corp. & Caledonia Soul Music.
Warner Bros. Music Ltd., 17 Berners Street, London W1.
All Rights Reserved. International Copyright Secured.

198

Verse

2. You can't stop us on the road to free-dom,
3. You can't stop us on the road to free-dom,

you can't keep us 'cause our eyes can see.
you can't stop us 'cause our eyes can see.

Men with in-sight, men in gran-ite,
Men with in-sight, men in gran-ite,

knights in ar-mour bent on chiv-al-ry.
knight in ar-mour in-tent on chiv-al-ry.

D.S. 𝄋
and fade

I'll tell a tale of old Manhattan
Adirondack bus to go
Standing waiting on my number
And my number's gonna show.

DADDY SANG BASS

Words & Music: Carl Perkins

dirt; We'd get to-geth-er in a fam-'ly cir-cle sing-in' loud. _____ Dad-dy sang

song; We'll be to-geth-er a - gain up yon-der in a lit-tle while. _____

F   C7   F

CHORUS

bass, ma-ma sang ten - or, me and lit-tle broth-er would join right in there;

F   F7   B♭   F

Sing - in' seems to help a troub-led soul. _____ One of these

F   C7   Gm7   C7

days, and it won't be long, I'll re - join them in a song; I'm gon-na

F   F7   B♭   F

join the fam 'ly cir - cle at the throne._____ No, the cir - cle ___ won't be bro - ken, _____ Bye and bye, Lord, bye and bye. ___ Dad-dy'll sing bass, ma-ma'll sing ten-or, me and lit-tle bro-ther will join right in there in the sky, Lord, ___ in the sky _____ Now I re - ___

F   C7   F   Bb   F   F
F   F7   Bb   F   C7
F   F7   Bb   F
F   Bb   C7   F

THE LETTER

Words & Music: Wayne Carson Thompson

wrote me a let - ter said she could-n't live_ with-out_ me no more._

Lis-ten mis-ter can't you see I got to get back_ to my ba - by once more,_ An - y way.

Give me a tick - et for an air - plane, Ain't got time_ to take the fast-est train.

Lone -ly days are gone,_ I'm a - go - in' home,_ My ba - by just wrote_ me a

1. let - ter._____ 2. Well she let-ter._ My ba -by just wrote_me a let - ter._ My

Repeat for fade

Repeat for fade

HARPER VALLEY PTA

Words & Music: Tom T. Hall

1. I want to tell you all a story 'bout a Harper Valley widow'd wife _____ who had a teenage _____ daughter who attended Harper Valley Junior High. _____ Well, her daughter came home one after-

(Recitation):

2. The note said, Mrs. Johnson, you're wearing your dresses way too high—
   It's reported you've been drinking and a-runnin' 'round with men and going wild.
   We don't believe you ought to be a-bringing up your little girl this way—
   It was signed by the secretary, Harper Valley P-T.A.

3. Well, it happened that the P-T.A. was gonna meet that very afternoon—
   They were sure surprised when Mrs. Johnson wore her mini-skirt into the room.
   As she walked up to the blackboard, I still recall the words she had to say.
   She said, "I'd like to address this meeting of the Harper Valley P-T.A.

4. Well, there's Bobby Taylor sittin' there and seven times he's asked me for a date.
   Mrs. Taylor sure seems to use a lot of ice whenever he's away.
   And Mr. Baker, can you tell us why your secretary had to leave this town?
   And shouldn't widow Jones be told to keep her window shades all pulled completely down?

5. Well, Mr. Harper couldn't be here 'cause he stayed too long at Kelly's bar again.
   And if you smell Shirley Thompson's breath, you'll find she's had a little nip of gin.
   Then you have the nerve to tell me you think that as a mother I'm not fit.
   Well, this is just a little Peyton Place and you're all Harper Valley hypocrites.
   No, I wouldn't put you on, because it really did, it happened just this way,
   The day my mama socked it to the Harper Valley P-T.A.

MOCKIN' BIRD HILL

Words & Music: Vaughn Horton

Moderately fast country waltz

Chorus

Tra-la- la, twit-tle-dee- dee- dee, it gives me a thrill To

wake up in the morn-in' to the mock-in' bird's trill; Tra-la- la, twit-tle-dee-

dee- dee, there's peace and good- will; You're wel - come as the flow -ers on

1. 2.
Mock- in' Bird Hill. 2. Got a
3. When it's

3.
Mock- in' Bird Hill.
slower

DANG ME

Words & Music: Roger Miller

wom - an sit - tin' home _____ with a month old _____ child. _____
lack _____ four - teen dol - lars hav - in' twen - ty sev - en cents.
pap - py was a pis - tol, I'm a son - of - a - gun. _____

Chorus

Dang me, dang me, they ought-ta take a rope and hang me

high from the high - est tree, Wom - an, would you weep for me!

After repeats
D. S. al Coda

Coda

211

BATTLE OF NEW ORLEANS

Words & Music: Jimmie Driftwood

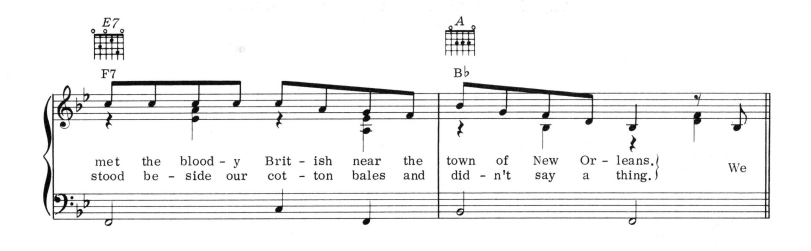

met the blood-y Brit-ish near the town of New Or-leans.}
stood be-side our cot-ton bales and did-n't say a thing.}
We

Chorus

fired our guns and the Brit-ish kept a-com-in', There wuz-n't nigh as man-y as they

wuz a while a-go. We fired once more and they be-gan to run-nin', On

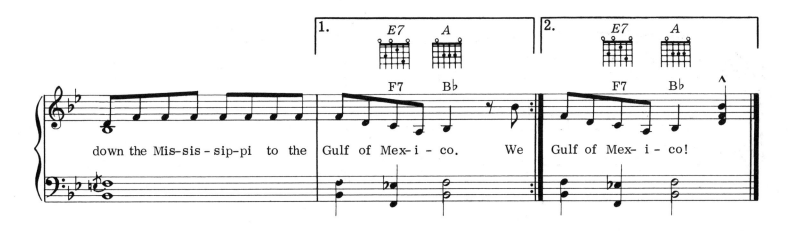

down the Mis-sis-sip-pi to the Gulf of Mex-i - co. We
Gulf of Mex- i - co!

WITH PEN IN HAND

Words & Music: Bobby Goldsboro

think I can't make ev-'ry-thing up to you, — Then I'll be gone and

you'll be on your own, _____ you'll be on your own. _____

3. Can you take good care of Johnny?
   Can you take him to school everyday?
   Can you teach him how to catch a fish and keep all those bullies away,
   Hear what I say?

4. Can you teach him how to whistle a tune?
   Can you tell him about the man in the moon?
   If you can do these things then maybe he won't miss me,
   Maybe he won't miss me.

5. And tonight as you lay in that big lonely bed,
   And you look at the pillow where I laid my head,
   With your heart on fire will you have no desire to kiss me,
   And to hold me?

6. And if you can forget the good times we had,
   If you think that the good times don't outweigh the bad,
   Then sign your name and I'll be on my way,
   I'll be on my way.

BEHIND CLOSED DOORS

Words & Music: Kenny O'Dell

hair hang _____ down, and she makes me glad I'm _____ a

man; _____ Oh, no one knows what goes on be-hind closed _____

doors. My be-hind closed _____ doors. _____

rit.------

2. My baby makes me smile, Lord, don't she make me smile.
   She's never far away or too tired to say I want you.
   She's always a lady, just like a lady should be
   But when they turn out the lights, she's still a baby to me.

KENTUCKY GAMBLER

Words & Music: Dolly Parton

who's gon - na raise____ your chil - dren in____ Ken - tuck - y,

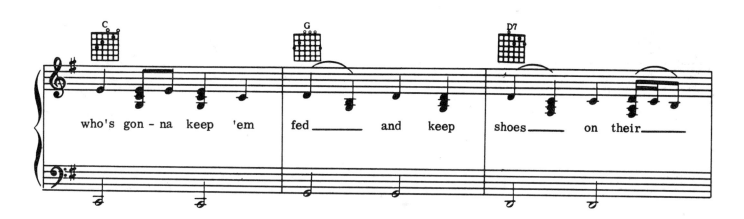

who's gon - na keep 'em fed____ and keep shoes____ on their____

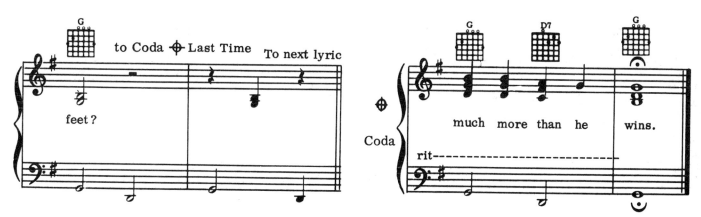

to Coda ⊕ Last Time   To next lyric

feet ?

Coda ⊕   much   more   than   he   wins.

rit-----------------------------

2. At gam'bling he was lucky, so he left Kentucky,
   Left behind his woman and his kids.
   Into the gay casino in Nevada's town of Reno,
   Kentucky Gambler planned to get rich quick.

3. At the gambler's paradise, Lady Luck was on his side;
   Kentucky Gambler played his cards just right.
   He won at everything he played, Kentucky Gambler had it made,
   And he should have quit and gone on home that night.

2nd Chorus: But you have the green-back dollar, sorrow's always bound to follow;
                Reno's dreams fade into neon amber,
                And Lady Luck, she'll lead you on,
                She'll stay awhile and then she's gone.
                You'd better go on home, Kentucky Gambler.

4. But a gambler never seems to stop 'til he loses all he's got,
   And so Kentucky Gambler, he played on, he played 'til he lost all he won.
   He was right back where he started from, then he started wantin' to go home.

3rd Chorus: Kentucky Gambler, there ain't nobody waitin' in Kentucky
                Where you ran out and someone else walked in.
                Kentucky Gambler, looks like you ain't really very lucky;
                Seems to me a gambler loses much more than he wins.

(Tag:)   Much more than he wins.

I'VE GOT A TIGER BY THE TAIL

Words & Music: Harlan Howard and Buck Owens

I've got a tiger by the tail, it's plain to see; I won't be much when you get thru' with me. Well, I'm a losing weight and a-turnin' mighty pale. Looks like I've got a tiger by the

VERSE

tail. _____

1. Well, I thought the day I met you, you were meek as a
2. Well, ev-'ry night you drag me where the bright lights are

lamb: Just the kind, to fit my dreams and plans. But now, the pace we're
found: ___There ain't no way to slow you down. ___ I'm a-bout as

liv-in' takes the wind from my sail; And it looks like I've got a tig-er by the
help-less as a leaf in a gail;

tail. _____ I've_ got_ a _

D. S. al ⊕ Coda

⊕ *Coda*

tail. _____

TOGETHER AGAIN

Words & Music: Larry Weiss

men, _____ I'm to-geth-er a - gain. _____ I got the
men, _____ I'm to-geth-er a -

gain. _____ You'll nev-er wit - ness this _____ man

break down and cry. _____ May - be I'll drop a tear _____ when

some-thing is caught in my _____ eye. _____ To-geth-er a - gain, _____ me and my -

self, _____ Wings on my shoes, los-in' my blues, be -in' my-

self. _____ May-be you're gone, _____ I say it a-

gain, _____ Ba-by, ba-by, a - men, _____ I'm to-geth-er a - gain.

Ba-by, ba-by, a - men, _____ I'm to-geth-er a - gain. Ba-by, ba-by, a-

Repeat and fade

226

ALL I EVER NEED IS YOU

Words & Music: Jimmy Holiday & Eddie Reeves

And lov-ing you is all I ask, Hon-ey, All I Ev-er Need Is You.

Win-ters come and they go, and we watch the melt-ing

snow. Sure as sum-mer fol-lows spring, all the things you do

give me a rea-son to build my world a-round you. Some men fol-low rain-bows, I am

CANDY KISSES

Words & Music: George Morgan

Moderato

1. CAN-DY KISS-ES _____ wrapped in pa - per _____ mean more to
2. cas - tle _____ out of dreams, dear _____ I thought that

you _____ than an - y of mine. _____ CAN-DY KISS-ES _____
you _____ were build-ing one too. _____ Now my cas - tles _____

_____ wrapped in pa - per, _____ you'd rath-er have them _____ an - y old
_____ all have fall - en, _____ and I am left _____ a - lone and

time._____ You don't mean it____ when you whis-per____
blue._____ Once my heart was____ filled with glad - ness,____

____ those sweet love words____ in my ear._____ {1.-2. CAN-DY
____ now there's sad - ness,____ on - ly tears._____

KISS - ES _____ wrapped in pa - per____ mean more to you____

____ than mine do dear._____ 2. I built a dear._____

GOLDEN ROCKET

Words & Music: Hank Snow

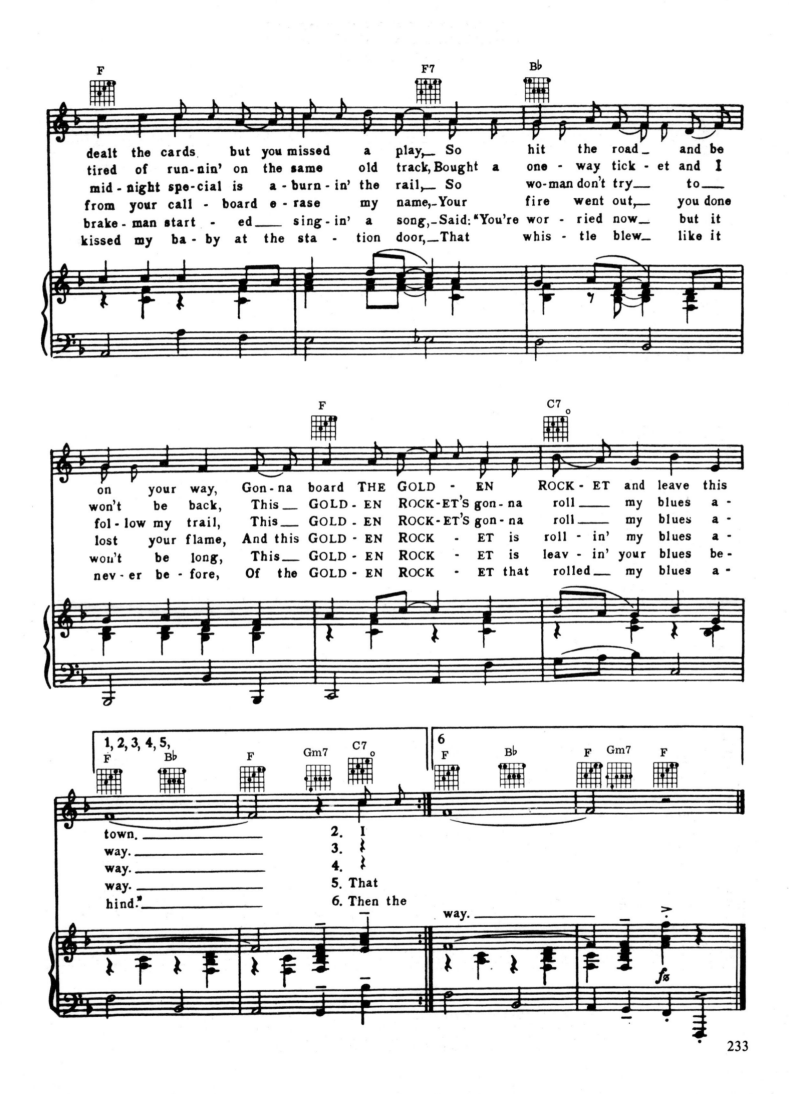

I'M MOVING ON

Words & Music: Hank Snow

On, _____ I'll soon be gone, _____ You were
on, _____ Oh, hear my song. _____ You had
on, _____ Keep roll - in' on. _____ You're gon -
On, _____ I'm roll - in' on. _____ You have
on, _____ You stayed a - way too long. _____ I'm

fly - in' too high for my lit - tle old sky ___ so I'M MOV - IN'
the laugh on me, so I've set ___ you free ___ and I'M MOV - IN'
na ease my mind, so put me there on time, keep roll - in'
bro - ken your vow and it's all o - ver now, ___ so I'M MOV - IN'
through ___ with you, too ___ bad you are blue, ___ so keep mov - in'

On. _____
on. _____
on. _____
On. _____
on. _____

2. That
3. Mis - ter
4. I
5. But

235

TAKE IT EASY

Words & Music: Jackson Browne & Glenn Frey

Take it ___ eas - ___ y, take it ___ eas - ___

y, ___ don't let the sound of your ___ own ___ wheels ___ drive you cra - ___ zy. ___

Light - en up ___ while you still ___ can, ___ don't e - ven try ___ to un - der - stand, ___

___ just find a place to make ___ your ___ stand ___ and take it eas - ___

Well, I'm a-stand-in' on a cor-ner in Wins-low, Ar-i-zo-na it's such a fine sight to see, it's a girl, my Lord, in a flat bed Ford slow-in' down to take a look at me. Come on, ba-by, don't say may-be,

238

I__ got -ta know if your__ sweet_ love_____ is gon - na save_____ me.__

We may lose__ and we may__ win, but we will nev-er be here a-gain,__

__ so o - pen up, I'm climb -in' in,__ so take it eas - y.__

Well, I'm a - run-nin' down the road try'n' to loos-en my load,__ got a world__

239

of trou-ble on my_ mind, look-in' for a lov-er who won't_

_ blow my cov-er, she's so_ hard to find._ Take it eas -

y, take it_ eas - y, don't let the sound of your_ own_

wheels_ make you cra-zy._ Come on,_ ba - by,_

241

GUESS THINGS HAPPEN THAT WAY

Words & Music: Jack Clement

I don't like it but I guess things hap-pen that way. _____

Fate gave me that girl to lean on; Then it put me on my own.
(God) (He)

Heav-en help me be a man and have the strength to stand a-lone.

I don't like it but I guess things happen that way.   2. You

WALK RIGHT IN

Words & Music: Gus Cannon & H Woods

Guitar chords used in this composition

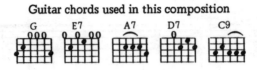

Slowly, with strong beat

1. Walk Right In, ____ set right ___ down, ____ Dad-dy, let your mind roll ___
2. Walk Right In, ____ set right ___ down, ____ Ba-by, let your hair hang ___

on. _____ Walk Right In, _____ set right ___ down, ___
down. _____ Walk Right In, _____ set right ___ down,

245

SMOKE! SMOKE! SMOKE! (That Cigarette)

Words & Music: Merle Travis & Tex Williams

247

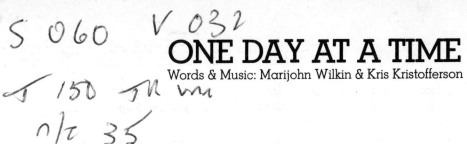

ONE DAY AT A TIME

Words & Music: Marijohn Wilkin & Kris Kristofferson

Moderate country waltz

Help me be - lieve in what I could
Well, Je - sus, you know if you're look - ing be -

be and all that I am.
low, it's worse now than then.

Show me the stair-way, I have to climb;
Push - in' and shov - in', crowd - ing my mind,

Lord, for my sake, teach me to
So for my sake, teach me to

take one day at a time. _____ One
take one day at a time. _____

day at a time, _____ Sweet Je - sus, _____ that's all I'm

ask - ing from you. _____ Just give me the strength to

do ev - 'ry day what I have to do. _____

Chorus

250

Yes - ter - day's gone, _____ Sweet Je - sus, _____ and to-
mor - row may nev - er be mine. _____ Lord,
help me to - day, show me the way one day at a

2nd time rall.

1. time. _____
2. time. _____

251

LONELY STREET

Words & Music: Kenny Sowder, Carl Belew & W.S. Stevenson

STREET. _____ Per-haps up-on that LONE-LY STREET, There's some-one such as I _____ Who came to bu-ry brok-en dreams and watch an old love die _____ If I could find that LONE-LY STREET, Where dim lights bring for-get-ful-ness, Where brok-en dreams and mem-ries meet, Where's this place called LONE-LY STREET. _____ I'm STREET. _____

rit.

CITY LIGHTS

Words & Music: Bill Anderson

Guitar chords used in this composition

1. The bright ar-ray of CI-TY LIGHTS As far as I can see, The
2. The world was dark and God made stars To bright-en up the night; Did the

great white way shines through the night For lone-ly guys like me. A
God who put the stars a - bove Make those CI - TY LIGHTS? Did He

ca - ba - ret, a honk-y tonk, Their flash-ing signs in - vite A
make a place for men to cry When things don't turn out right? Are we

bro-ken heart to lose it-self In the glow of CI-TY__ LIGHTS. Lights that say "For-
just sup-posed to run and hide Be-hind those CI-TY__ LIGHTS? Lights that say "For-

get her__name in a glass of sher-ry wine;" Lights that of-fer oth-er__girls for
get her__love in a dif-ferent at-mos-phere" Lights that lure are noth-ing__but a

emp-ty hearts like mine; They paint a pret-ty pic-ture of a world that's gay and
mas-que rade for tears; They paint a pret-ty pic-ture but my arms can't hold them

bright, But it's just a mask for lone-li-ness Be-hind those CI-TY LIGHTS. The
tight, And I just can't say, "I love you to a street of CI-TY LIGHTS."

Fox Trot
S. 088   V032
T 150 TR-2
mc35 1/2/3/2

YOU ARE MY SUNSHINE

Words & Music: Jimmie Davis & Charles Mitchell

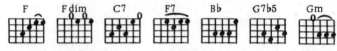

The oth - er night dear ___ as I lay dream - ing, ___ I dreamt that
once dear ___ there'd be no oth - er, ___ And no one
love you ___ and make you hap - py, ___ If you will

you were by my side, ___ Came dis - il - lus - ion ___ when I a -
else could come be - tween, ___ But now you've left me ___ to love an -
on - ly do the same, ___ But if you leave me ___ how it will

TIE A YELLOW RIBBON 'ROUND THE OLE OAK TREE

Words & Music: Irwin Levine & L. Russell Brown

you re-ceived my let-ter tell-in' you___ I'd soon be free,___
real-ly still in pris-on and my love___ she holds the key,___ a

then you'll know just what to do___ if you still want me,
sim-ple yel-low rib-bon's what I need to set me free, I

if you still want me.
wrote and told her please.

Chorus:

Tie a yel-low rib-bon round the ole oak tree,___ it's been

three long years, do ya still want me? ___   If

I don't see a rib-bon round the ole oak tree ___   I'll

stay on the bus, for-get a-bout us, put the blame on me,   if

I don't see a yel-low rib-bon round   the ole___ oak

tree.___

tree.___ Now the whole damn bus is cheer - ing and I

can't be - lieve I see a hun - dred yel - low rib - bons round the

ole _____ oak _____ tree.___

261

COUNTRY GIRL

Words & Music: Neil Young

No time to stay__ the same,   Too young to   leave, _____

No pass out sign   on the door   set me think-

ing   Are wait-ress-es pay-ing the price of their wink-ing, _____

___ While stars   sit in bars and de-cide   what they're drink-ing, ____

263

They drop by to die 'cause it's fast-er than sink-ing, _____

Too late to keep the change, Too late to pay, _____

No time to stay the same, Too young to leave, _____

Find out that now was the an-swer to an-swers that you _____ gave lat-er, _____

She did the things that we both did be-fore,_ now, but who _____ for-

gave her. _____ If I could stand to see her cry - ing I would tell her

not to care. When she learns of all your ly - in' will she join you

DADDY DON'T YOU WALK SO FAST

Words : Peter Callender
Music: Geoff Stephens

"Dad-dy don't you walk so fast,——————— Dad-dy don't you walk so fast——

Dad-dy slow down some,—— 'cos you're mak -in' me run,————

Dad-dy don't you walk so fast"——————

It   If   on - ly for the sake of my sweet

daugh-ter,———— I just had to turn back home right there and then,—————————— And

try to start a new life with the moth-er of my child, I could-n't bear to hear those words a-

-gain, as she said "Dad-dy don't you walk so fast, _____ Dad-dy don't you walk so fast,_

_____ Dad-dy slow down some ___ 'cos you're mak-in' me run, ___

Dad-dy don't you walk so fast, ___ Won't you slow down some ___ 'cos you're mak-in' me run, ___

Dad-dy don't you walk so fast" _____

MAMA YOU BEEN ON MY MIND

Words & Music: Bob Dylan

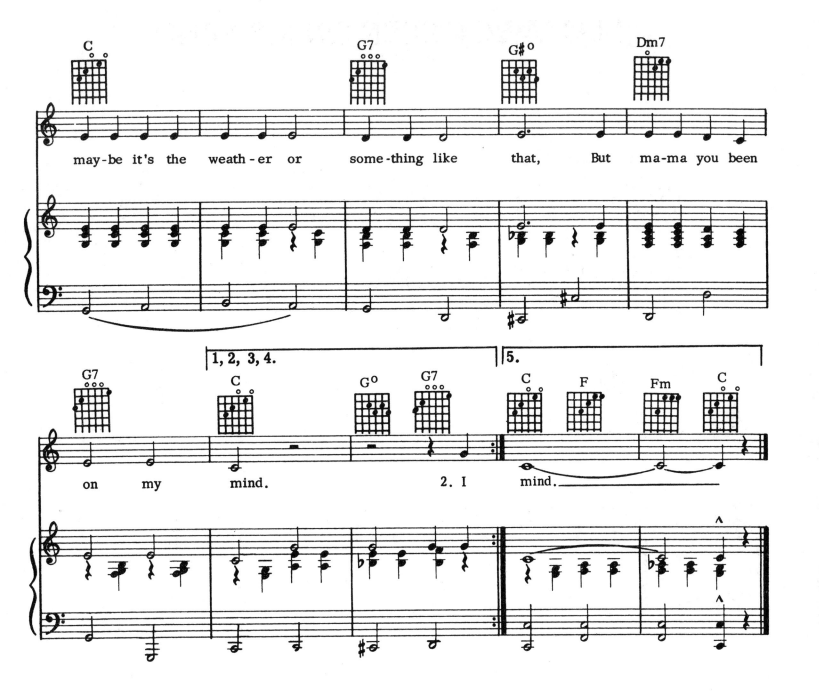

2. I don't mean trouble, please don't put me down or get upset
   I am not pleadin' or sayin', "I can't forget"
   I do not walk the floor bowed down an' bent, but yet,
   Mama, you been on my mind.

3. Even tho my mind is hazy an' my thoughts they might be narrow
   Where you been don't bother me nor bring me down in sorrow
   It don't even matter to me where you're wakin' up tomorrow
   But mama, you're just on my mind.

4. I am not askin' you to say words like "yes" or "no",
   Please understand me, I got no place for you t' go,
   I'm just breathin' to myself pretendin' not that I don't know
   Mama, you been on my mind.

5. When you wake up in the mornin', baby, look inside your mirror
   You know I won't be next to you, you know I won't be near
   I'd just be curious to know if you can see yourself as clear
   As someone who has had you on his mind.

THE LAST WORD IN LONESOME IS ME

Words & Music: Roger Miller

Slowly, with feeling

The last word in lone-some is me, the last word in lone-some is me. My heart is as lone-ly as a heart can be lone-ly, The last word in lone-some is me.

Too bad what's hap-pened ___ to our good love, ___ too bad what's hap-pened ___ to our good love. Some-times our best is-n't quite good e-nough, and the last word in lone-some is me. ___

D.S. al ⊕ Coda

My heart is as lone-ly as a heart can be lone-ly, The last word in lone-some is me. ___

molto rit.

273

THE LOVELIEST NIGHT OF THE YEAR

—Music Adapted: Irving Aaronson. Words: Paul Francis Webster

Slowly

Refrain, Slowly

When you are in love _____ It's THE LOVE - LI - EST

NIGHT OF THE YEAR _____ Stars twin - kle a -

bove _____ And you al-most can touch them from here _____

Thrilled by the won-der of you _____ And the won-der-ful touch of your hand And my heart starts to beat _____ Like a child when a birth-day is near _____ So, kiss me my sweet, _____ It's THE LOVE-LI-EST NIGHT OF THE YEAR. _____ YEAR. _____

GREEN RIVER

Words & Music: John C. Fogerty

danc-in' in the moon - light.   I can hear the bull   frog

call-in' me.   Won-der if my rope's still hang-in' to the tree.

Love to kick my feet   'way   down the shal-low wat-er.

Shoe fly, drag - on fly,   get back t'your moth-er.   Pick up a flat rock,   skip it a-cross   Green

Riv-er._____ Up at Co-dy's camp I spent my days

With flat car rid-ers and cross_____ tie walk-ers.

Old Co - dy, Jun - ior took me o - ver. Said,"You're gon - na find the world_

_ is smoul - d'rin'. If you get lost come on home_ to Green Riv-er."_____

WHAT'S HE DOIN' IN MY WORLD

Words & Music: Carl Belew, Eddie Bush & B.J. Moore

and what's he do - in' in my world?

What's he do - in' in my world?

Did you tell him that you're my girl? If your

love is real-ly true tell him my world's made for two,

IF YOU LOVE ME (Let Me Know)

Words & Music: John Rostill

stay. If you love me let me know.— If you don't—

— then let me go.— I can't take— an-oth-er min-

ute of a day— with-out you in— it. If— you

love me, let it be,— If you don't — then set me free.-

Take the chains ____ a - way that keep me lov - in' you. ____

____ The arms that o - pen wide ____ to hold me clos-

er; ____ The hands that run their fin-

gers through my hair; ____ The smile that says hel - lo, ____

it's good to see you. Any time I turn a-round

to find you there. It's this and so much more

that makes me love you.

What else can I do to make you see? You

know you have___what-ev - er's mine___ to give you,   but a

love af - fair___for one_____ can nev - er be._____   If   you

D.S. 𝄋 al ⊕ Coda

Coda

Ah! Take___ the chains_

____ a - way___ that keep me lov - in' you._____

rit. -------

FIRE AND RAIN

Words & Music: James Taylor

Chorus:

291

TEACH YOUR CHILDREN

Words & Music: Graham Nash

2. Teach Your Children well
   Their father's hell
   Will slowly go by
   And feed them on your dreams
   The one they picks
   The one you'll know by.

   (To Bridge and Interlude)

3. And you, of the tender years
   Can't know the fears
   That your elders grew by
   And so please help them with your youth
   They seek the truth
   Before they can die.

4. Teach your parents well
   Their children's hell
   Will slowly go by
   And feed them on your dreams
   The one they picks
   The one you'll know by.

   (To Bridge and Coda)

BETTER LOVE NEXT TIME

Words & Music: Steve Pippin, Johnny Slate & Larry Keith